David Beckham

Roy Apps

Illustrated by Chris King

FRANKLIN WATTS
LONDON•SYDNEY

Chapter One:

Wonder Goal!

It's a cold, bright winter's morning and there's a boys' football match going on. A few spectators huddle on the touchline, stamping their feet to keep warm.

Suddenly, the ball comes to the smallest player on the pitch; a skinny boy with spiky, blond hair. He's on the halfway line. He traps the ball, looks up and sees three opposition players charging towards him. They are all much bigger than him. In a split second he makes a decision.

He arches his body sideways, swings his right leg back and kicks the ball hard and high over the rest of the players. It seems to bend through the air and then hang there for a moment before dropping behind the goalkeeper and into the...

"GOAL!" shout the spectators.

The boy is mobbed by his team mates. The supporters jump up and down in excitement. One of the spectators, whose son is playing for the opposition, turns to the man standing next to him.

"Did you see that? The ball travelled half the length of the pitch! And the way he got it to bend! Who is he?"

"His name's David Beckham."

"That was a wonder goal! You know, that lad's something special."

The man turns towards the visiting spectator with a smile. "Yes, I think he is," he says. "But then I would. I'm his dad."

Ridgeway Rovers – that's the team ten-year-old David Beckham was in. They were something special, too: the most successful boys' football team in northeast London. They had won the County league and the County cup, and once went 92 games unbeaten.

After the match the Ridgeway boys talked about their dreams.

"Who are you going to play for, David, Spurs or Arsenal?"

"Neither," replied David Beckham. "I'm going to play for Man United."

His team mates hooted with laughter. "You're weird," one of them said. "Man United? They're even more rubbish than Spurs. Anyway, Manchester's miles away. What do you want to go up North for?"

David frowned. Put like that, it did seem like a stupid dream to want to play for Manchester United. Why did he want to play for them so much? "I suppose it's because my dad's a Man United supporter," he said with a shrug.

"Is he? Why?"

"I don't know."

"He must have a reason," laughed David's friend.

"Yes, I suppose he must," agreed David.

Chapter Two:

The Busby Babes

That afternoon, David found his dad in the front room. He was reading the football reports in the Sunday newspaper. David went over and sat next to him.

"Dad, why are you a Man United supporter? None of the other dads around here are."

David's dad put the newspaper down. "I'll tell you why," he said.

"When I was a boy, my dad was an Arsenal supporter. We listened to the football results on the radio every Saturday teatime. I just loved the sound of the words 'Manchester United'. So I started to listen out for Manchester United's results.

"It was a poor club. They couldn't afford to buy players, so they developed their own young talent. They were nicknamed 'the Busby Babes' after their manager, Matt Busby. My favourite player was Duncan Edwards. He was only 21, but he already had eighteen England international caps. I had his picture above my bed.

"Manchester United were the first English team to play in the European Cup. They played Red Star Belgrade in the quarter finals. They won at Old Trafford and had to draw the return match in Belgrade to make it through to the semi finals.

"The morning after the match, my dad – your grandad – came in to wake me up on his way to work. 'It was 3–3,' he said. 'Manchester United are through!' I was so excited.

"But that evening, when my dad came home from work, his face was white.

"I remember him saying, 'I'm sorry son. There's very bad news. About Manchester United.'

"'What's happened?' I asked.

"'Their plane stopped for refueling at Munich airport. It crashed on take off. Most of the squad have been killed or injured. It's a terrible thing.'

"Eight United players died at Munich, including my hero, Duncan Edwards. I took his picture down from my bedroom wall and replaced it with one of Bobby Charlton, one of the players who had survived. And that's why your second name is Robert; you were named after Bobby Charlton."

David had listened to his dad's story in silence. After a bit, he said:

"Dad, one day I'm going to play for Manchester United."

Chapter Three:

Murdering Mum's Flowers

David lay on the sofa reading *Shoot!* magazine. He could hear his parents talking in the kitchen.

"You shouldn't encourage him with all this Manchester United nonsense," his mother was saying.

"But he's keen," his dad said.

"Oh, I know he's keen," said his mum. "He's round the park playing football at all hours and even when he's at home he spends all of his time in the back garden, using his little sister as a goalkeeper. Every time a shot goes wide, he murders one of my flowers."

"But very few of his shots do go wide, do they?" his dad said. "That's the point. David's good. Good enough to be a professional."

"He may be good, but he's so little. I've seen professional footballers. They're a hard bunch. David will end up being kicked from one end of the pitch to the other. And Manchester of all the daft places! It's the other end of the country! If he's going to become a footballer, what's wrong with Tottenham or Arsenal?"

"It's what the boy wants," his dad replied, "it's his dream."

"I know," said his mum, "that's what worries me. If the dream doesn't work out for him, he's going to end up so disappointed. It's him I'm thinking of."

David got up from the sofa. His mum was right. He was small for his age and Manchester was miles away. Since Ridgeway Rovers had been doing so well, team scouts from Leyton Orient, West Ham, Arsenal and Spurs had all come to watch their matches. But nobody had come from Manchester United. Why should they? The North of England was full of talented young footballers. Manchester United scouts didn't need to come to London. But if they didn't come to London, David wondered, how would he ever be spotted?

One day, David was watching *Blue Peter* on TV. There was a man with the presenters whose face David recognised instantly. It was Bobby Charlton, the Manchester United and England legend. His dad's hero. One of the Busby Babes who had survived the Munich air crash.

Bobby Charlton was talking. "So any lad who fancies his chances can come to Old Trafford and take part in the Bobby Charlton Soccer School. The three winners will get to train with the Manchester United squad."

David knew what he had to do. "Mum!" he yelled through to the kitchen. "Mum! I've got to go to Old Trafford!"

Chapter Four:

The Bobby Charlton Soccer School

David said goodbye to his mum, dad and sisters at the gates to Old Trafford.

"Give it your best, son," said his dad. "You're good enough to do really well here."

The Bobby Charlton Soccer School was very
different to Ridgeway Rovers. There were
hundreds of boys there from all over the
world. David was the smallest and the
youngest – just ten years old. He felt
very alone, very lost and very homesick.
In training, drills and practice matches
people only noticed him to say, "That kid's
little, isn't he?" He didn't score any wonder
goals. He didn't look special.

At the end of the Soccer School, three boys
won the chance to train with Manchester
United. David Beckham wasn't one of them.

At home, for months afterwards, nobody mentioned Manchester United. David thought his dream was over. But he carried on training, practising and playing.

The following year, his mum and dad got a letter about the next Bobby Charlton Soccer School.

"I want to go, Mum," said David.

"But David, you went last year and got homesick," sighed his mum.

"Yes, but I'm older now – and bigger," David pointed out.

"Not that much bigger," said his mum.

This time there were even more boys from all over the world, and David was still the youngest and the smallest of them. But this time everything was familiar and David knew what to expect. He played well; so well, that he won the final with the highest score ever in the history of the Bobby Charlton Soccer School tournament.

David's parents were watching from the stands.

"I can hardly believe it," whispered his dad. "My son, out there on the Old Trafford pitch, shaking hands with Bobby Charlton. Bobby Charlton, whose picture I had on my wall when I was a boy!"

After the Soccer School they travelled back down to London. More matches, more practising; more dead flowers in the back garden. But still no scouts from Manchester United turned up at Ridgeway Rovers. David started training with Spurs. Old Trafford seemed a very long way away.

Then one Saturday afternoon, David played a schools' match at Waltham Forest. His mum was waiting for him in the car park and when he got in the car, he saw that she had been crying.

"What's the matter, Mum?" he asked.

"Good job you had a good match today," she sniffed.

"Why?"

"See that brown car over there?"

David looked to where his mum was pointing. A tall man in a suit was getting out of an old brown Ford Sierra. He walked towards them. David's mum wound down the window. The man put his head through and smiled at David.

"Hi, David. My name's Malcolm Fidgeon. I'm a Man United scout. Alex Ferguson would like to meet you."

Chapter Five:

Old Trafford

After his first meeting with Alex Ferguson –
the United manager – David trained in
Manchester during the school holidays.

"You've got talent, David," Alex Ferguson told
him, "but more than that, you're a hard
worker. Your character is a credit to you and
to your mum and dad."

David's mum beamed. "Thank you," she said. "It's just such a pity that Manchester's such a long way away."

Alex Ferguson nodded. "Tell you what," he said. "Every time we've got a match in London, you can come and watch us play. You can meet the players and staff, have a pre-match meal with them, really get to know the club."

But David carried on training with Spurs every week.

Then David and his parents were called in to see the Spurs manager, Terry Venables.

"We'd like to sign you, David," he said. Then he turned to David's parents. "We can offer him a six-year deal and a £70,000 signing-on fee."

Seventy thousand pounds? That would be enough to buy me a Porsche when I'm 17, David thought.

Terry Venables put his hand out to shake on the deal.

"I'd like to think about it," said David.

David liked Spurs; the staff were very friendly and he'd enjoyed training with the team. Not only that, the club was just 15 minutes from his house. If he joined them, he wouldn't have to move away from home. But Spurs wasn't his dream.

A few weeks later, on his 13th birthday, David and his parents were driven up to Manchester to meet Alex Ferguson.

"How are you, David?" asked Alex Ferguson. "And how are your little sister's goalkeeping skills coming on?" Already Alex Ferguson seemed like an old friend. "We'd like to sign you, David," he said. He didn't mention any signing-on fee. He didn't need to. David took out a pen and signed.

David's parents were over the moon. But his dad was also cautious.

"You may have signed for Man United, but you haven't done anything yet. When you've played for the first team, then we'll talk about you having achieved something."

Three and a half years later David Beckham made his first appearance for the Manchester United first team. He came on for the last 17 minutes of a League Cup match against Brighton.

He didn't get another first team game for another two years, when he played in a European Cup match. Would he ever achieve his dream of becoming a Manchester United player?

Not long after the European Cup game, David was called into Alex Ferguson's office.

"David," said Alex Ferguson, "I've got some news for you."

Chapter Six:

First Team

"Dad, the boss wants me to go on loan to Preston North End." David had rung his dad as soon as Alex Ferguson had told him the news. "I think he wants to get rid of me."

"Rubbish!" said David's dad. "He wants you to get more experience – toughen you up a bit."

But deep down he wondered if his son might be right.

David enjoyed his time with Preston in Division Three. He scored his first-ever league goal, from a free kick against Doncaster Rovers in March 1995.

"We wouldn't mind having you for the rest of the season," the Preston manager told him.

At the end of his loan period, David went to see Alex Ferguson. It was the first time he'd ever asked to see the boss.

"I'd like to stay at Preston," he told the Manchester United manager.

Alex Ferguson leapt up from his chair. He was furious. "You're not going anywhere, son!" he roared at David. "We've got an injury crisis. You're in the squad against Leeds on Saturday."

On Saturday 2nd April 1995, David Beckham started his first-ever League game for Manchester United. His family were there to watch him, of course. It turned out a rather boring 0–0 draw. But that didn't matter to David. He was now playing first-team football for Manchester United: his dad's club, Bobby Charlton's club, the Busby Babes' club.

His club.

Fact file
David Beckham

 Born: Leytonstone, London, 2 May 1975

 Married: 4 July 1999 Victoria Adams

 Children: Brooklyn (born 2 March 1999)
Romeo (born 1 September 2002)
Cruz (born 21 February 2005)

8 July 1991	Joins Manchester United as a trainee
23 September 1992	Manchester United First team debut; Coca Cola Cup v Brighton & Hove Albion
22 January 1993	Signs as a professional with Manchester United
7 December 1994	Champions league debut v Galatasaray
19 August 1995	First Premiership goal v Aston Villa
1 September 1996	First full England International debut v Moldova
26 June 1998	First goal for England v Colombia
15 November 2000	Captains England for the first time v Italy
13 June 2003	Awarded OBE
1 July 2003	Signs for Real Madrid. He scores on his debut
January 2008	Signs for LA Galaxy
26 March 2008	Wins 100th cap for England in their game against France

DREAM TO WIN — Lewis Hamilton

Lewis looked out of the kitchen window and frowned. Weird things were happening at the bottom of the garden. Over the last few weeks his dad's shed had grown. There was a new end and brand new double doors along one side. His dad was out in the shed now, but just what he was doing there Lewis had no idea. When he asked Linda, his step-mum, she said:

"Your grandad's coming to stay and we thought he might like to sleep in the shed, so your dad's fixing it up with a shower and loo."

Lewis knew she was joking. The shed was where Lewis's dad tested and repaired the remote-control cars that Lewis raced. Lewis was a champion remote-control car racer. He'd even been on *Blue Peter*. He was hoping to get a brand new remote-control car for Christmas.

**Continue reading this story in
DREAM TO WIN: Lewis Hamilton**